Nuffield Primary Science
SCIENCE PROCESSES AND CONCEPT EXPLORATION

Ages
5-7

Sound and music

TEACHERS' GUIDE

PUBLISHED FOR THE NUFFIELD–CHELSEA CURRICULUM TRUST BY COLLINS EDUCATIONAL

Contents

Explanation of symbols in the margins

!	Warning	**it**	Opportunities for children to use information technology
AT 1	Good opportunities to develop and assess work related to Experimental and Investigative Science.	**e**	Equipment needed
t	Notes which may be useful to the teacher	**pb**	Reference to the pupils' books
v	Vocabulary work		

CHAPTER 1

Planning

1.1 The SPACE approach to teaching and learning science

A primary class where the SPACE approach to science is being used may not at first seem different from any other class engaged in science activities; in either, children will be mentally and physically involved in exploring objects and events in the world around them. However, a closer look will reveal that both the children's activities and the teacher's role differ from those found in other approaches. The children are not following instructions given by others; they are not solving a problem set them by someone else. They are deeply involved in work which is based on their own ideas, and they have taken part in deciding how to do it.

The teacher has, of course, prepared carefully to reach the point where children try out their ideas. She or he will have started on the topic by giving children opportunities to explore from their own experience situations which embody important scientific ideas. The teacher will have ensured that the children have expressed their ideas about what they are exploring, using one or more of a range of approaches – from whole class discussion to talking with individual children, or asking children to write or draw – and will have explored the children's reasons for having those ideas.

With this information the teacher will have decided how to help the children to develop or revise their ideas. That may involve getting the children to use the ideas to make a prediction, then testing it by seeing if it works in practice; or the children may gather further evidence to discuss and think about. In particular, the teacher will note how 'scientific' children have been in their gathering and use of evidence; and should, by careful questioning, encourage greater rigour in the use of scientific process skills.

It is essential that it is the children who change their ideas as a result of what they find themselves, and that they are not merely accepting ideas which they are told are better.

By carefully exploring children's ideas, taking them seriously and choosing appropriate ways of helping the children to test them, the teacher can move children towards ideas which apply more widely and fit the evidence better – those which are, in short, more scientific.

You will find more information about the SPACE approach in the Nuffield Primary Science *Science Co-ordinators' handbook*.

1.2 Useful strategies

Finding out children's ideas

This guide points out many opportunities for finding out children's ideas. One way is simply by talking, but there are many others. We have found the following strategies effective. How you use them may depend on the area of science you are dealing with. In the teachers' guides you will find examples of these strategies, with suggestions as to where you might use them. More information about them is given in the *Science Co-ordinators' handbook*.

Talking and open questioning

Whole class discussions can be useful for sharing ideas, but they do not always give all children a chance to speak. It is often helpful if children are allowed to think of their own ideas first, perhaps working them out in drawings, and are then encouraged to share these with others – perhaps with just one other child, or with a larger group.

Annotated drawings

Asking children to draw their ideas can give a particularly clear insight into what they think. It also gives you a chance to discuss the children's ideas with them. Words conveying these ideas can then be added to the drawing, either by you or by the child, in the course of discussion to clarify what has been represented. Such work can be kept as a permanent record.

Sorting and classifying

This can be a useful way of helping children to clarify their ideas and to record their thinking. They could sort a collection of objects or pictures into groups.

Writing down ideas

When they have acquired some writing skill, this gives children the opportunity to express their own views. It will usually be in response to questions posed by you.

Log books and diaries

These can be used to record changes over a longer period of time. They need not necessarily be kept by individual children, but could be kept by a group or class as a whole. Children can jot down, as words or drawings, the changes they notice and something about what they think are the reasons for what they observe.

Helping children to develop their ideas

Letting children try out their own ideas

This will involve children in using some of the process skills of science: at first mainly observing, predicting, and communicating. Later, as children approach Key Stage 2, they will begin to make more use of measuring, hypothesizing, planning and carrying out fair tests, and interpreting results and findings.

As often as possible, children should see what happens when they put their ideas to test. They should be encouraged to observe and report carefully what happens and to give their ideas about why it happens.

Encouraging generalization from one context to another

In discussing a particular event, for example dissolving sugar in tea, consider whether the explanation proposed applies in another context, such as salt dissolving on a wet road. You or the children might suggest other contexts where the idea might be tried. This might be done by discussing the evidence for and against the explanation, or by gathering more evidence and testing the idea in the other context, depending on children's familiarity with the events being examined.

Discussing the words children use to describe their ideas

Children can be asked to be quite specific about the meaning of words they use, whether scientific or not. They can be prompted to think of alternative words which have almost the same meaning. They can be asked to think of examples of a word they are using, such as 'melt', so that you can decide when to introduce alternative or more precise words if necessary.

Extending the range of evidence

Some of the children's ideas may be consistent with their experience up to that time, but they could be challenged by extending the range of this experience. This applies particularly to things which are not easily observed, such as slow changes; or those which are normally hidden, such as the insides of objects. Books are useful in some cases.

Getting children to communicate their ideas

Expressing ideas in any way – through writing, drawing, modelling or, particularly, through discussion – involves thinking them through, and often rethinking and revising them. Discussion has a further advantage in that it is two-way and children can set others' ideas against their own. Just realizing that there are different ideas helps them to reconsider their own.

1.3 Charts to help children to develop their ideas

The chart on page 23 shows how you can help children to develop their ideas from starting points which have given rise to different ideas.

The centre rectangles contain starter questions.
The surrounding 'thought bubbles' contain the sort of ideas expressed by children.
The further ring of rectangles contains questions posed by teachers in response to the ideas expressed by the children. These questions are meant to prompt children to think about their ideas.
The outer rounded boxes indicate ways in which the children might respond to the teacher's questions.
Some of the shapes have been left blank, as a sign that other ideas may be encountered and other ways of helping children to develop their ideas may be tried.

1.4 Sound and music and the curriculum

Making sounds, hearing sounds

This theme shows ways in which young children might begin to explore their ideas about sound.

Young children commonly believe that sound is caused by a physical action, such as hitting a drum with a stick. Sometimes they may suggest that specific features of the sound maker are responsible for the sound, such as the wood or the skin of the drum. Young children rarely notice the sound maker vibrating. They often mention that they hear sounds because they are listening. Many will point out that they hear sounds because of their ears and some will draw a larger ear when they are hearing louder sounds. KS1 children may be unaware that sounds travel. A few children will indicate that sounds travel to them by a single thread which avoids objects on its path. This thread of sound may go direct to them or to other people who are also listening.

Within this theme children have the opportunity to experience a variety of everyday sounds and to make sound makers. They should exchange ideas about how sounds are made, how they might be grouped together or altered. There are suggestions of how, by using other senses such as touch and sight, children can be helped towards an understanding that a movement is necessary in an object for sound to occur. Through investigation and discussion, children can begin to understand how sounds are made, how they are heard, and that sounds travel. In KS2 they will continue to develop their understanding of how sounds are made, received and transmitted.

Physical Processes

3 Light and sound
c that there are many kinds of sound and many sources of sound;
d that sounds travel away from sources, getting fainter as they do so;
e that sounds are heard when they enter the ear.

Understanding Energy and Forces (Stages P1 to P3)

Forms and sources of energy
• heat, light and sound which pupils can detect with their own senses.

Properties and uses of energy
• everyday uses of these forms of energy in common devices.

1.5 Experimental and Investigative Science

Two important aspects of children's learning in science are:

◆ learning how to investigate the world around them;
◆ learning to make sense of the world around them using scientific ideas.

These are reflected in the National Curriculum. 'Experimental and Investigative Science' covers the first aspect. The second aspect is covered by the rest of the Programme of Study. Although these two aspects of science learning are separated in the National Curriculum they cannot be separated in practice and it is not useful to try to do so. Through investigation children explore their ideas and/or test out the ideas which arise from discussion. As a result, ideas may be advanced, but this will depend on the children's investigation skills. Thus it is important to develop these skills in the context of activities which extend ideas. So there is no separate Nuffield Primary Science teachers' guide on scientific investigations, because opportunities to make these occur throughout all the guides and they form an essential part of the SPACE approach.

AT 1

Thus in this guide you will find investigations which provide opportunities to develop and assess the skills and understanding set out in Experimental and Investigative Science. These are marked in the text by the symbol shown here. In this teachers' guide, the investigation which covers the most skills is 'Altering sounds' (page 28).

It is important that teachers give active guidance to pupils during investigations to help them work out how to improve the way in which they plan and carry out their investigations.

Experimental and Investigative Science is about the ways scientific evidence can be obtained, about the ways observations and measurements are made, and about the way in which the evidence is analysed. It therefore sets out three main ways in which pupils can develop their ability to do experimental and investigative science, as follows:-

1 'Planning experimental work'. Here, children should be helped to make progress from asking general and vague questions, to suggesting ideas which could be tested. Teachers' discussion with pupils should aim to help them to make predictions, using their existing understanding, on the basis of which they can decide what evidence should be collected. This should lead them to think about what apparatus and equipment they should use.

When children describe plans for their work, they should be helped to think about what features they are going to change, what effects of these changes they are going to observe or measure, and what features they must keep the same. In this way they can come to understand what is meant by 'a fair test'.

2 'Obtaining evidence'. Children should make observations in the light of their ideas about what they are looking for and why. When they describe their observations, teachers may have to help them to improve, for example by reminding them of their original aims and plan for the work. Such help should also encourage progress from qualitative comparisons and judgements to appreciating the value of making quantitative measurements (for example 'cold water' is qualitative, 'water at 12°C' is quantitative). This should lead to the development of skills with a variety of instruments and to increasing care and accuracy in measurement, involving, for example, repeating measurements to check.

3 'Considering evidence'. Here, children should first learn to record their evidence in systematic and clear ways, starting with simple drawings and then learning to use tables, bar charts and line graphs to display the patterns in numerical data. Then they should be asked to think about and discuss their results, considering what might be learnt from any trends or patterns. As ideas develop, they should be careful in checking their evidence against the original idea underlying the investigation and should become increasingly critical in discussing alternative explanations which might fit their evidence. In such discussions, they should be helped to relate their arguments to their developing scientific understanding. They should also be guided to see possibilities for conducting their investigation more carefully, or in quite different ways.

Whilst these three may seem to form a natural sequence of stages, children's work might not follow this particular sequence. For example, some might start with evidence from their observations and proceed on this basis to propose a hypothesis and a plan to test it. For others, the results of one task may be the starting point for a new inquiry involving new measurements. Useful learning about how to investigate might arise when only one or two of the above aspects of an investigation are involved, or when the teacher tells children about some aspects so that they can concentrate on others. However, there should be some occasions for all pupils when they carry out the whole process of investigation by themselves.

The assessment examples given in chapter 3 are analysed in relation to the level descriptions, which describe children's progress in relation to these three aspects: *planning experimental work*, *obtaining evidence* and *considering evidence*. Thus, these three provide a framework both for guiding children and for assessing their progress in experimental and investigative work.

1.6 Resources

This is what you may need to carry out the investigations shown in this book.

Materials for constructing simple 'sound makers', such as large bottle tops, spoons, elastic bands, plastic tubs, a variety of seeds or dried foods.
Photographs, magazine pictures showing ways in which people and animals hear.
Tape recorders.
Collection of sound makers such as tambourines, triangles and musical instruments from other cultures.

1.7 Warnings

Activities which need particular care are indicated by this symbol in the margin. Everything possible should be done to ensure the safety of the children during their investigations. You should consult any guidelines produced by your own Local Education Authority and, if your school or LEA is a member, by CLEAPSS. See also the Association for Science Education publication *Be safe! some aspects of safety in school science and technology for Key Stages 1 and 2* (2nd edition, 1990). This contains more detailed advice than can be included here.

The points listed below require particular attention.

Avoid sound-making items which might be swallowed. Use seeds from health food shops which will not be treated with toxic pesticides, and do not use red kidney beans.
Children must not poke sharp or small items into their ears, because of the risk of damaging the ear drum and infection.
Particular care must be taken when using ear plugs.
Very loud noises should not be made close to anyone's ear as this may impair their hearing.
Investigations which involve comparisons of children's hearing ability should be carried out with discretion and sensitivity.

1.8 Planning your science programme in school

The following pages give examples of how two schools have planned their science programme for the whole of Key Stage 1. Planning of this kind helps to provide continuity and progression in children's learning in science. The development of such whole school programmes is discussed more fully in the *Science Co-ordinators' Handbook*.

Each plan covers the requirements for the National Curriculum at Key Stage 1 and shows which themes in the Nuffield Primary Science Teachers' Guides have been used for planning the topic in detail by the classteacher.

Example 1

This primary school has recently grown from 1.5 form entry to 2 form entry and so have had to take account of varying class sizes and vertical grouping. Their programme is based on fixed year topics which provide progression through the programme of study but by using the SPACE approach staff feel they are able to cater for individual children.

Each topic is planned out, by year group, in terms of the concept to be explored and the key ideas to be focused on using the Teachers' Guides. Some topics run for one term whilst others are restricted to half a term. A minimum of five lessons are allowed for each half term. Individual teachers use the topic plan to develop their own short term planning responding to the ideas of the children in their class.

	AUTUMN TERM	SPRING TERM		SUMMER TERM	
RECEPTION	Individual variation	Sources and uses of electricity	Light and dark	Changing materials	
Nuffield Primary Science Teachers' Guide	The variety of life 2.2	Electricity and magnetism 2.1	Light 2.1, 2.2	Materials 2.2	
Programme of Study †	Sc2:4a	Sc4:1a	Sc4:3a, b	Sc3:2a, b; Sc4:2d	
YEAR 1	Pushes and pulls	Making and hearing sounds	The human body and keeping healthy	Local habitats	Plants and animal growth
Nuffield Primary Science Teachers' Guide	Forces and movement 2.1 Using energy 2.2	Sound and music 2	Living processes 2.2	Living things in their environment 2.1 Rocks, soil and weather 2.1 Earth in space 2.3	Living processes 2.3
Programme of Study †	Sc4:2a, b, c, d	Sc4:3c, d, e	Sc2:2a, b, c, d, e, f	Sc2:5a, b	Sc2:2e; 3a, b, c
YEAR 2	Properties of materials	Magnets	Electricity - simple circuits	Naming and grouping living things	
Nuffield Primary Science Teachers' Guide	Materials 2.1 Rocks, soil and weather 2.1	Electricity and magnetism 2.3	Electricity and magnetism 2.2	The variety of life 2.1	
Programme of Study †	Sc3:1a, b, c, d, e	Sc3:1b, c	Sc4:1a, b, c	Sc2:1a, b; 4b	

Example 2

Situated in a large conurbation this primary school is 2.5 form entry but the number of children entering fluctuates from year to year causing difficulties with class size. The Nursery is an integral part of the school and work is shared with the Reception classes. Therefore this pre-YR1 time is planned as a whole providing a wide range of experiences for the children so that they are 'working towards' the requirements of the programme of study.

The plan is set out by year group and the different elements of the Programme of Study, covering five topics per year with each one to be covered in approximately half a term. Each year group decides the order of their topics during the year. The provision of a 'spare' half term allows teachers some flexibility in their planning and, if they wish, to introduce other aspects of science not prescribed by the National Curriculum.

	AUTUMN TERM		SPRING TERM		SUMMER TERM	
RECEPTION	This is me	Our school	Plants and animals	Homes - using electricity	Toys	
Nuffield Primary Science Teachers' Guide	The variety of life 2.2	Living things in their environment 2.3	Living things in their environment 2.1; Living processes 2.3	Electricity and magnetism 2.1	Forces and movement 2.1	
Programme of Study (working toward) †	Sc2:2a, b, f; 4a	Sc2:1a, 3b, 5a; Sc3:2a	Sc2:1b, 3a, b, c, 4b, 5a, b	Sc4:1a, 3a, b	Sc4:2a, b, c	
YEAR 1	Ourselves	Growing things	Materials - clothes	Sounds/Night and day	Floating and sinking	
Nuffield Primary Science Teachers' Guide	Living processes 2.2; Variety of life 2.2	Living processes 2.3	Materials 2.1	Sound and music 2; The earth in space 2.1	Forces and movement 2.2	
Programme of Study †	Sc2:1b; 2a, b, e, f; 4a, b	Sc2:3a, b, c	Sc3:1a, b, c, d, e; 2a	Sc4:3c, d, e	Sc3:1a, c, e; Sc4:2a	
YEAR 2	Keeping healthy	Habitats	Materials - homes	Light and electricity	Moving things	
Nuffield Primary Science Teachers' Guide	Living processes 2.2	The variety of life 2.1; Living things in their environment 2.1; Rocks, soil and weather 2.1	Materials 2.1; 2.2	Electricity and magnetism 2.1, 2.2; Light 2.1; 2.2	Forces and movement 2.1; Using energy 2.2	
Programme of Study †	Sc2:1b; 2b, c, d	Sc2:4b; 5a, b	Sc3:1a, b, c, d, e; 2b	Sc4:1a, b, c; 3a, b	Sc4:2a, b, c, d	

† For the purposes of these charts the references to sections of the Programme of Study have been abbreviated as follows:
Sc2 = Life Processes and Living Things
Sc3 = Materials and their Properties
Sc4 = Physical Processes

1.9 Planning a topic

Here is a case study which may help you in planning a topic.

Case study: Communication

The teacher had decided to place children's study of sound within a topic 'Sounds and communication'. The teacher regarded sound as an extensive area of study, with children engaged in a large number of investigations. Focusing specifically on this one area of science helped the teacher to manage children's learning and support the development of their ideas about sound. Although the emphasis within the topic was to be how sounds are made and how sounds reach people so that they are heard, the teacher did identify some opportunities to make links with other curriculum areas.

SCIENCE

Sound

◆ The class of children went on a listening walk and recorded all the sounds they noticed.

◆ They discussed how the sound got to them so that they heard it and how the sound was made.

◆ Sounds that were heard during the walk were sorted into loud and quiet sounds.

◆ Children's ideas about sounds being made were followed up by finding different ways of making sounds. These sound makers were used to communicate sounds in nursery rhymes.

◆ The effect of being close to or further away from a sound was explored.

◆ Sounds used in the environment and at home to communicate a message were considered, such as alarms, bells, radio, telephone.

◆ Some children explored their ideas about sounds travelling through different materials to find the most effective material for a telephone.

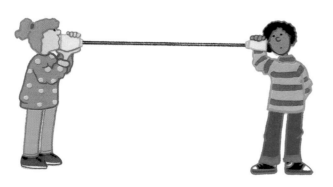

English

◆ Children collected pictures of different ways of sending information. They sorted them into those which used sound and those which didn't.

◆ Children made a collection of greetings cards for different occasions.

◆ The class had close links with another school and sent a message using audiotape.

◆ Children designed their own signs to communicate information.

Music

◆ A variety of experiences of music was provided within the topic. Children listened to classical, rock and folk music.

◆ In addition they were able to make sounds using familiar instruments and instruments from other cultures.

Geography

◆ The sound walk led to a consideration of why different sounds were heard in different places. Children investigated the direction of the sounds they heard.

◆ A sound plan was developed showing pictures of sounds made in and around school.

◆ Children noticed the different signs in the environment and discussed the meaning of each sign.

History

◆ The development of different ways of sending messages was explored, including beacons, messages in bottles, carrier pigeons, telephones, letters, telegrams, television, radio.

◆ The story of Alexander Graham Bell helped children understand about a real person in history.

1.10 Pupils' books

The pupils' book accompanying this guide is called *A First look at sound and music*. The pupils' books are intended to be used spread by spread. The spreads are not sequential, and they are covered in these notes in thematic order.

Features of the pupils' books include:
◆ Stimulus spreads, often visual, designed to raise questions, arouse curiosity, and to promote discussion.

◆ Information spreads, which give secondary source material in a clear and attractive way.

◆ Activity ideas, to form the basis of investigations to be carried out by the children.

◆ Cross-curricular spreads and stories which can act as a basis for creative writing, or spreads with a historical or creative focus.

◆ Real life examples of applications of science in the everyday world.

Musical sounds pages 2–3

Purpose: To help children discuss musical instruments and the fact that sound can be made in different ways, using a variety of instruments.
Notes: Discuss the different categories of instruments: percussion (things you hit), string (things you pluck), woodwind (things you blow) and why the instruments are categorized in this way.
Extension activities: Collect instruments in the school and discuss them, what category they are in and what sound they make. Make instruments from various materials.
Teachers' guide cross-references: *Sound and music*, pages 11, 28.

Peace and quiet pages 4–5

Purpose: A starting point for a discussion of sound in a natural environment.
Notes: Discuss the sounds the children would hear in this environment and contrast these with the sounds in the school.
Extension activity: Read other poems about sound.
Teachers' guide cross-references: *Sound and music*, pages 24-5.

What a lot of noise! pages 6–7

Purpose: To introduce children to a discussion about more noises and where they are coming from.
Questions for discussion: In the picture, what is making a noise? What are the noises like? Which noises do you prefer? Which do you dislike?
Extension activity: Encourage the children to write their own poems about sound.
Teachers' guide cross-references: *Sound and music*, pages 24-5.

Animal ears pages 8–9

Purpose: A 'wow' spread to introduce them to the idea that there is a distinction between the inner ear and the outer, protective flap around it.
Note: The frog's ear is the raised, round shape below the eye.
Extension activities: Children could try to waggle their own ears. They could talk about their pets and any class pets. Visit a zoo or farm to look at other animals (but check on school policy first). Discuss safety and ears, such as not poking things into them, not listening to sounds that are too loud on personal stereos.
Teachers' guide cross-reference: *Sound and music*, page 30.

Listen, everyone! pages 10–11

Purpose: To introduce children to the concept that sound travels and that it can be amplified (made louder).
Notes: The devices for amplification shown here are a microphone, a megaphone, a hearing aid and an ear trumpet. This spread should raise awareness of hearing difficulties.
Pupils' book cross-reference: A first look at electricity and magnets, pages 22-3.
Teachers' guide cross-references: Sound and music, pages 30-1.

Stephen's day pages 12–13

Purpose: To inform, in story form, about how hearing aids work and to raise awareness of hearing difficulties.
Notes: Ask the children to imagine what it would be like to be deaf – they could try to empathize with Stephen.
Extension activity: Some children with hearing difficulties might be willing to describe their experiences and explain the equipment they use.
Teachers' guide cross-references: Sound and music, pages 10-11, 30-1.

Sound puzzle pages 14–15

Purpose: A matching activity to extend children's vocabulary directly linked with sound.

Bells pages 16–17

Purpose: A starting point for a discussion of the way in which bells are used as signals.
Note: Make the distinction between the real (hand-held school bell) and the electronic (telephone).
Extension activity: Children could discuss and identify bells in their homes and in school, which may not be in the pictures.
Teachers' guide cross-reference: Sound and music, page 31.

Body sounds pages 18–19

Purpose: An enjoyable activity in which children can find out more about the sounds their own bodies make.
Notes: This is a good starter activity to introduce children to sound. There are useful pictures around the edge of the page.
Teachers' guide cross-reference: Sound and music, page 25.

Someone to play with pages 20–21

Purpose: A story to help children think about the different sounds encountered when visiting friends.
Extension activity: Help children make this into a drama, in which they mimic the sounds suggested in the cartoon.
Teachers' guide cross-references: *Sound and music*, pages 10-11, 18.

Sounds like… pages 22–23

Purpose: To introduce children to words that rhyme (or sound alike).
Notes: In this poem, examples are given of rhyming words. This will help children to find the pairs of rhyming words on the opposite page. These range in difficulty from the basic (house/mouse), to the intermediate (sea/tree) and the difficult (toe/dough).
Teachers' guide cross-reference: *Sound and music*, page 26.

CHAPTER 2

Making sounds, hearing sounds

AREAS FOR INVESTIGATION

◆ Exploring a wide range of ways of making sounds.

◆ Investigating ways of altering sounds.

◆ Experiencing the variety of sounds that can be heard in the environment.

KEY IDEAS

◆ Sounds can be high or low, loud or soft.

◆ Sound can be detected by sensitive instruments, which include the human ear.

◆ Sound spreads out in all directions.

◆ *Sound can be reflected from surfaces and so can produce echoes.

◆ *Sound travels, and takes a measurable time to do so.

◆ *Sound travels through solids, liquids and gases.

◆ *Sound is caused by vibrations in a material.

(*Asterisks indicate ideas which will be developed more fully in later key stages.)

A LOOK AT
sound and music

Sounds are made when things move. These movements can be seen when a ruler is twanged or an elastic band is plucked. Sounds can be altered by changing the length, thickness or tension of the moving material. Sounds can be made louder through causing bigger movement, for example by striking an object harder.

Sounds can be received by instruments such as the ear or a microphone. Sounds travel through materials.

Sometimes you can make a sound which is heard immediately, and then again, after a short interval. The second sound occurs when the sound bounces back off some surface. This reflected sound is an echo.

Finding out children's ideas
STARTER ACTIVITIES

1   Using instruments in the classroom

Collect a variety of sound makers and place them in a bin liner or a large box. Encourage children to guess what's in the bag. Bring out the sound makers individually and let the children handle them.

Q *What is this made of?*
What do you notice about the instruments?
How do you think the sound is made?
How do you know that it is making a noise?
Can you sort the sound makers into groups?
Which makes the loudest/softest sound?
Can you make the sound louder/softer?

2   Listening to sounds

Ask the children to draw pictures to represent some of the sounds they can hear in the classroom or playground. Talk to the children as they are drawing. They could do this after a listening walk.

Q *How do you think the sound is made?*
How do you hear the sound?

Children may include in their drawings an indication that sound travels. Clarify these ideas by asking:

Q *Can you tell me what is happening in your drawing?*
How do you think that happens?

3   Echoes

Find out what the children understand by an echo:

Q *When have you heard an echo?*
How does an echo happen?
Could you draw a picture to show where you might notice an echo?
Can you show what is happening to the sound?

Children's ideas

1 Making sounds

Children sometimes explain that a sound is made, without including any suggestions about how sound occurs. They may not notice any movement taking place when the sound is made.

Children commonly explain that they have plucked, shaken or hit the sound maker.

Children often describe the physical attributes of the sound maker, recognizing that these are responsible for the sound occurring. The child who drew the top drawing overleaf has identified the importance of the metal in sound production; she is aware of the movement of the ball inside the bell.

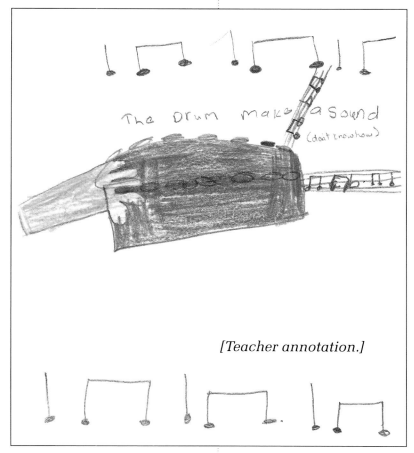

The Drum make a sound (don't know how)

[Teacher annotation.]

Sound coming out of drum

The drum makes the music if you hit the drum and then it does make a loud sound.

The drum makes the music if you hit the drum and then it does make a loud sound.

[With teacher annotation.]

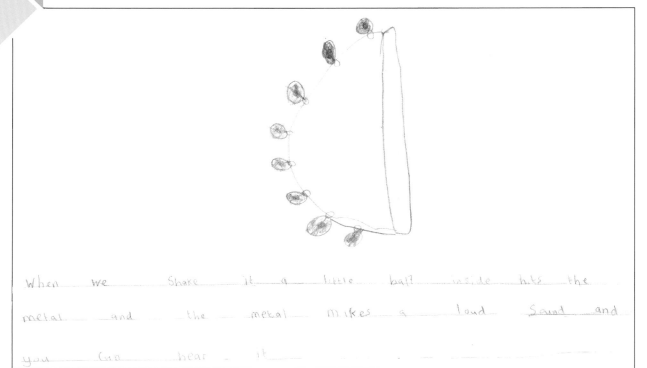

When we Shake it a little ball inside hits the metal and the metal mikes a loud Sound and you Can hear it

2   Hearing sounds

Children often explain that it is important to be listening in order to hear the sound. They may believe that the sound travels only to someone who is listening for it. Sometimes children include large ears in their drawings to indicate that loud sounds are being heard, or that a person is listening more intently. They may draw a line to show the sound travelling to the ear. Often children draw a single line which goes to the ear, avoiding any obstacles, suggesting that they believe that sound only travels when nothing is in its way. Sometimes the sound is understood as travelling to one person. Occasionally, as in the example at the top of the next page, a child

The guitar is playing and he's listening.

might begin to show an awareness that sound moves in different directions.

Some children try to describe what happens inside the ear when we hear things. They may suggest that inside our heads we are able to sort out what sounds we hear, or what a sound is like. A minority suggest that sound goes through the ear into the brain, causing us to hear.

The bird opens its mouth The sound goes into your brain. The brain is tricky it can sort it out. The sound goes in your ear Then it goes down your neck

[Teacher annotation.]

3 Echoes

Children might be able to describe where echoes can occur and how they experience echoes, but they are rarely able to explain how an echo is produced. Many children suggest that echoes can be heard in caves, tunnels, and empty rooms. They draw echoes in large, empty, enclosed spaces. Their explanations often focus on how they experienced the echo, describing it as a noise which is repeated. Children's drawings might show the sound gradually decreasing.

Hello   Hello   Hello Hello

HELLO

A few children at this stage may reveal some understanding that sound can be reflected by describing an echo as a sound which hits something and comes back.

Teacher:	*What happens when you hear an echo?*
Child:	*You shout and it hits something and it vibrates off it.*
Teacher:	*Where would you hear an echo?*
Child:	*You'd hear it in a cave, subway, in a room with no furniture. It's echoey because it's hollow, it's got nothing in it.*

ecos are when your in a cave or something and its hollow so it says it alot

Hello

Hello Hello

say its load cause

Its hollow so it ecows

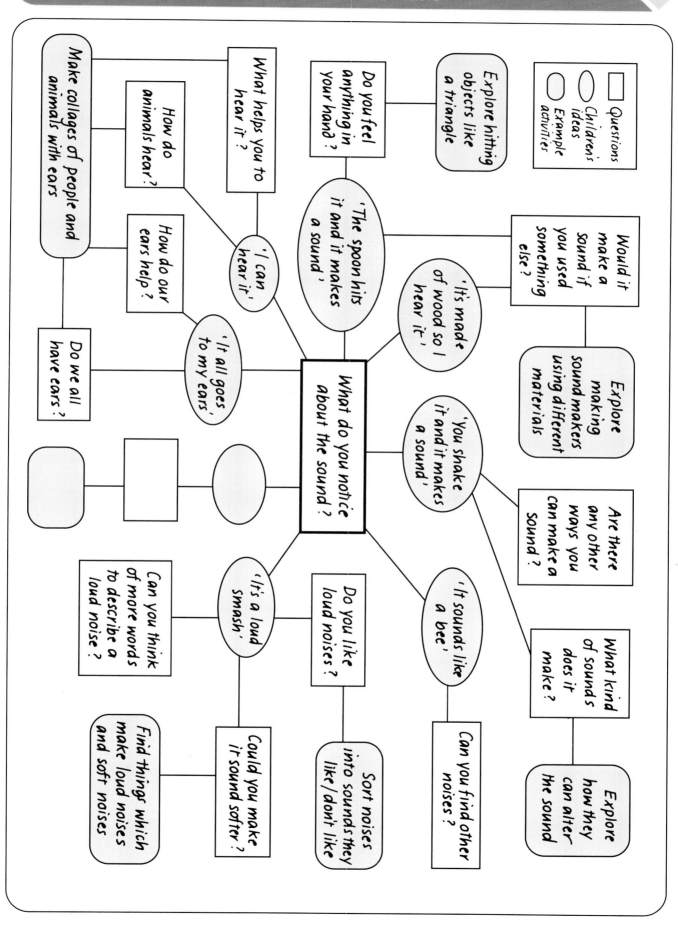

Make collages of people and animals with ears

What helps you to hear it?

How do animals hear?

How do our ears help?

Do we all have ears?

Explore hitting objects like a triangle

Do you feel anything in your hand?

'I can hear it'

'It all goes to my ears'

'The spoon hits it and it makes a sound'

'It's made of wood so I hear it'

Would it make a sound if you used something else?

Explore making sound makers using different materials

What do you notice about the sound?

'You shake it and it makes a sound'

Are there any other ways you can make a sound?

'It's a loud smash'

Can you think of more words to describe a loud noise?

Do you like loud noises?

'It sounds like a bee'

What kind of sounds does it make?

Find things which make loud noises and soft noises

Could you make it sound softer?

Sort noises into sounds they like/don't like

Can you find other noises?

Explore how they can alter the sound

Questions

Children's ideas

Example activities

23

Helping children to develop their ideas

The chart on the previous page shows how you can help children to develop their ideas from starting points which have given rise to different ideas.

1 A listening walk

Children's experience and ideas about sounds could be developed on a walk around the school. Ask them to identify all the sounds they hear during the walk. Children could tape record some of the sounds. Ask questions to encourage children to think about the variety of sounds they hear, as follows.

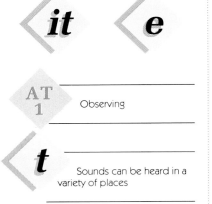

it *e*

AT 1 Observing

t Sounds can be heard in a variety of places

Q *How are we going to remember what sounds were like?*
What can you hear in the playground?
What do you notice in the school fields?
What do you hear in the secretary's office?
What do you notice in the kitchen?
What sounds are there in the classroom?

Encourage children to consider whether sound travels, and how, by asking:

Q *How do you hear the sound the [bird] is making?*
Can anyone else hear the sound?

Children will have experienced a wide variety of sounds during the walk. In the classroom they might be able to draw pictures of some of the sounds they have heard. These can be put together into a sound book.

A *first look at sound and music* contains examples of words that describe sounds and could be used for information or as the basis for discussions about representing different sounds.

A class discussion may reveal that some sounds are heard in only one place. Children could decide which sounds were heard in the same place.

Children could play back the recordings they have made during the sound walk. They could discuss the sounds.

 What sounds can you hear?
Which sounds are loud sounds?
Which sounds are quiet sounds?

A *first look at sound and music* encourages children to think about the sounds that might be heard in busy or quiet places, and has a story in which many different sounds are described.

2   Making sounds with our bodies

Let the children explore all the sounds they can make with different parts of their bodies.

A *first look at sound and music* can be used as a starting point for this activity and provides material for further discussions.

Give them an opportunity to discuss the ways in which they made the sounds.

Q *How did you make these sounds?*
Did you notice anything moving when you made the sound?
Could someone tell if you were clapping even if they couldn't hear you?

t   Some sounds are loud, others are quiet

   pb

   pb

3 Nursery rhymes

Ideas about sounds can be explored through nursery rhymes or songs.

Q *What noise would you hear as Mary waters her garden?*
What noise would Humpty Dumpty make when he falls?
What sounds would the Grand Old Duke of York's men make?
What noise would Jack's falling bucket make?

Children could make pictures of the nursery rhymes and write the words they use to describe the sounds next to the pictures.

A first look at sound and music contains examples of words that rhyme. This could provide the basis for further discussions about rhymes.

4 Making sound makers for sound effects

Provide children with suitable materials and encourage them to make their own sound makers.

Q *Can you make something which sounds like Humpty falling?*
Can you make something that sounds like the Grand Old Duke of York's medals?
Can you find a way to make the sound of the brown paper to fix Jack's head?
Can you make sounds to go with 'The wise man and the foolish man'? (This song is in A first look at rocks, soil and weather.)

AT 1   Communicating

! Children may swallow small items, or stick them into their ears or up their noses. Children should be careful when using elastic bands

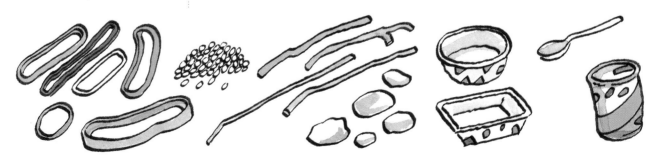

Groups of children could use their sound makers to accompany the rhyme or song.

AT 1 — Communicating

5 Sorting sounds

Children could sort their sound makers according to the ways in which they make sounds.

Q *Which sound makers do you pluck?*
Which sound makers do you bang?
Can you put together all the ones you can blow?
Are there any that you shake?

AT 1 — Observing

They might also sort them according to the kinds of sounds they make.

Q *Do all the sound makers sound the same?*
Can you sort them into ones that make loud and soft sounds?

t — There is a variety of sounds

AT 1 — Observing

6 Altering sounds

Children could attempt to change the sound of their sound makers.

Q *Can you make it sound louder or softer? Higher or lower?*
What happens to the sound if you strike it with
something else?
What happens to the sound if you use a different
elastic band?
Can you tell if it is making a noise even if you can't hear it?

Give the children an opportunity to discuss what they noticed about the ways the sounds were altered, and what this had to do with the changes they made to the sound makers.

Children could fill shakers with different materials such as beads, rice, hundreds and thousands or sugar, to find the loudest or quietest sound they can make.

A first look at sound and music contains examples of musical instruments, and encourages children to think about the ways in which sounds are produced in different instruments.

AT
1 General

Warn children that very loud sounds will permanently damage their hearing

pb

7 Identifying sounds

A guessing game will help children think about how sounds are made. A child could choose a sound maker and use it to make a noise without the other children seeing what is being used. The other children should guess how the sound is made. A series of questions will focus children's thinking.

Q *What do you notice about the sound?*
Is it loud or soft?
How do you think the sound is made?
What do you think is inside the sound maker?

AT 1 — Hypothesizing

e

AT 1 — Interpreting results and findings

You might play a tape recording of different sounds, such as a vacuum cleaner, running water, a child talking.

Q *What sounds can you hear?*
Which sounds were easy to name?
Why were some sounds more difficult?

How did you know the name of the sounds?
How did you hear the sounds?
What happens when the sound reaches your ear?

8 Likes and dislikes

Talk about which sounds children like and which they do not. Ask them to make a class collage showing the sounds they like and don't like. Help them to think about their own and others' choices through class discussion.

AT 1 — Communicating

Q *What sounds do most people like?*
What sounds do most people dislike?

Some children might carry out a survey about noises that people in the school dislike. They might ask other questions, such as:

Q *Do some noises make you happy?*
Do some make you feel cross?
What could people do to stop the noise?

They could present their findings as a picture graph or as a radio programme. Children could use a tape recorder to help them with the presentation.

9 Animals' hearing

Children could collect pictures of people and animals, and find out and compare how their ears differ.

Q *Do all the animals have ears that are the same shape or size?*
Do all the animals have ears in the same place?
How do ears help the animals?

A few children might see that some animals have no visible external ears. They might use secondary sources to find out whether these animals can hear.

A first look at sound and music provides information about animals' ears and their hearing.

10 Hearing difficulties

This issue should be treated sensitively

A class discussion could consider when we use our hearing and the differences that hearing difficulties might make to our life.

pandas eat bamboo..

AT
1 Interpreting results and findings

Q *Can you understand the television when the sound is turned down?*
How could people tell us things if we could not hear very well?

A first look at sound and music provides information about ways in which we make ourselves heard, and has a story about a day in the life of a boy with severe hearing difficulties.

(top right corner marker) **2**

Children might explore how to care for their ears, through secondary sources or by talking to the school nurse. They might make posters to encourage people to look after their hearing. (This could be linked to work on 'The human body and keeping healthy' in the *Living processes* teachers' guide and pupils' book.)

11 Sounds as signals

Ask children to think of sounds which are used to attract our attention and what these sounds might mean. They could talk about some of the following

A first look at sound and music encourages children to think about the ways in which bells give us information.

pb

12 Travelling sounds

Encourage children to think about how sound travels.

At home how do you know when the doorbell is ringing?
Where might you be when the doorbell rings?
Can you hear the bell in different parts of the house?
Can people in other rooms hear the bell too?
Why do you think people in different rooms hear the bell?

Let children investigate whether sound travels. Some could investigate whether people in different places can hear a particular sound.

Can you find out whether people in different places can hear the same sound?
How does the sound get to that person so they can hear it?

AT 1 — Communicating Hypothesizing

t — Sound travels in all directions

AT 1 — General

Using the climbing apparatus children could find whether sound travels to different heights.

To test whether sounds can travel through materials such as wood children could test whether they can hear sounds through closed doors.

13 Echoes

Ask children to consider the places where they might hear an echo. They may begin to realize that these places are similar in certain ways.

Q *What's special about the places where you might hear an echo?*
What do you think causes the echo?
Is the echo the same as the sound?
What happens to the sound?
How does the sound come back to you so you can hear it?
How is it the same as the sound? How is it different?

CHAPTER 3

Assessment

3.1 Introduction

You will have been assessing your children's ideas and skills by using the activities in this teachers' guide. This on-going, formative assessment is essentially part of teaching since what you find is immediately used in suggesting the next steps to help the children's progress. But this information can also be brought together and summarized for purposes of recording and reporting progress. This summary of performance has to be in terms of National Curriculum level descriptions at the end of the key stages, and some schools keep records in terms of levels at other times.

This chapter helps you summarize the information you have from children's work in terms of level descriptions. Examples of work relating to the theme of this guide are discussed and features which indicate activity at a certain level are pointed out to show what to look for in your pupils' work as evidence of achievement at one level or another. It is necessary, however, to look across the full range of work, and not judge from any single event or piece of work.

There are two sets of examples provided. The first is the assessment of skills in the context of the activities related to the concepts covered in this guide. The second deals with the development of these concepts.

3.2 Assessment of skills (AT1)

Things to look out for when pupils are investigating things to do with sound and music, indicating progress from level 1 to level 3:

Level 1: Making observations of simple properties of things which make sounds and of the kinds of sounds they make; talking about and drawing them.

Level 2: Making suggestions as well as responding to others' suggestions about how to find things out or compare sounds in terms of their pitch and loudness. Using equipment, such as musical instruments or tape-recorders, to make observations. Recording what they find and comparing it with what they expected.

Level 3: Saying what they expect to happen when something is changed and suggesting ways of collecting information to test their predictions. Carrying out fair tests, knowing why they are fair, and making measurements. Recording what they find in a variety of ways; noticing any patterns in it.

A teacher of Year 2 class provided the children with a variety of sources of sound and asked them to explore how each one made a sound. The teacher also asked some of the children to try to make a drawing showing:

How does the sound get to you so that you can hear it?

Their drawings were similar to the ones shown on pages 20 and 21. In discussing them with the teacher some children made these statements:

> *Julie:* When you bang the drum the sound goes in your ear.
>
> *Samantha:* The sound [from the electronic keyboard] goes through the gaps.
>
> *Gerard:* The vibrations [in the string telephone] can't go up slopes.

Julie's statement simply relates hearing to the ear, recalling something she already knows rather than making a prediction or a suggestion which could be investigated.

In Rebecca's account of the experiment shown in Gerard's picture she simply reported what she heard: *'I said hello Michael and Michael said hello Rebecca'.* Her work in this investigation was at level 1.

Gerard's work uses the evidence of Rebecca being able to hear Michael to conclude that vibrations can go up and down. Thus he explicitly compares what was found with what he expected. He understood what was being investigated and interpreted the results accordingly, indicating work at level 2.

Gerard

first we used thin meterial then we put
more layers of meterial to make it thicker
and see if we can hear it. we have
used a carrier bag we put the carrier
bag over were the sound was coming out
and pressed a button.

material	what happend
thin carrier	We could hear through
	the thin carrier
thick carrier	✓
silk carrier	✓
and hand.	✓

Gareth and Samantha

Gareth and Samantha made a series of observations, with different layers of material to test their suggestion. They observed whether the sound could be heard for each kind of layer. They recorded what they found and although did not explicitly interpret their results in terms of whether or not sound travels through things other than 'gaps', their work was at level 2. There was no attempt at measurement or fair testing, as required at level 3, but both of these would have been difficult in the context of this investigation. Thus the teachers would have to use other opportunities to encourage and assess their progress towards level 3.

3.3 Assessment of children's understanding (Part of AT4)

In terms of the work relating to sound and music, progression from level 1 to level 3 is indicated by:

Level 1: Identifying a variety of sounds and their sources.

Level 2: Recognising differences between sounds; comparing them in terms of pitch and loudness, and relating them to their sources. Knowing that sound travels from its source and is heard when it enters the ear.

Level 3: Knowing that sound is made when an object vibrates. Attempting to explain why some sounds are louder than others and sound different from each other, in terms of the position and kind of the source of the sound. Being aware that sound travels through various materials.

Christopher's drawing shows ways of making sound, but gives no indication of what makes the sound. Therefore his work has not yet reached level 1.

whispering

clapping

running

jumping

Christopher

Following exploration of various sound makers, Ian (drawing shown opposite) was able to compare different sounds. He noticed that moving his fingers could make the sound higher or lower. He also had ideas about sound travelling, albeit in roundabout ways, and that it is heard when it reaches the ear. These are all indications of achievement at level 2.

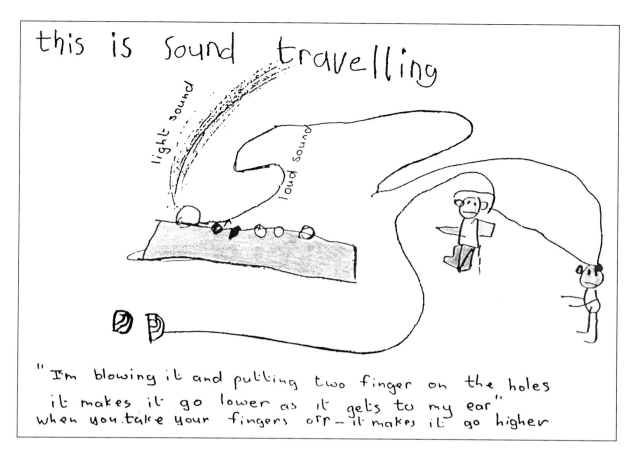

this is sound travelling

light sound

loud sound

"I'm blowing it and putting two finger on the holes
it makes it go lower as it gets to my ear"
when you take your fingers off – it makes it go higher

Ian

Rachel varied the sound made in bottles by having different amounts of water in them. Although she does not seem certain whether to describe the changes as from high to low or loud to soft, this shows progress towards level 2. Both Rachel and Ian would benefit from discussion of sources of sound where vibration is more obvious, in strings and drums, for example, so that they may begin to associate sound with vibration and make progress towards level 3.

The bottles make a diffrent noise because they had a different amount of water in them. The ones with a little bit of water in them made a loud noise and the ones with a lot in them made a low noise

Rachel

Index